This is London. Who lives here?

Wendy, John, and Michael live in London.

They live in a big house.
They are in bed.

Peter Pan and Tinker Bell are in London.

They come to the big house. They go in.

Peter Pan and Tinker Bell
fly in the bedroom.

Peter Pan likes this house.
The bedroom is big.

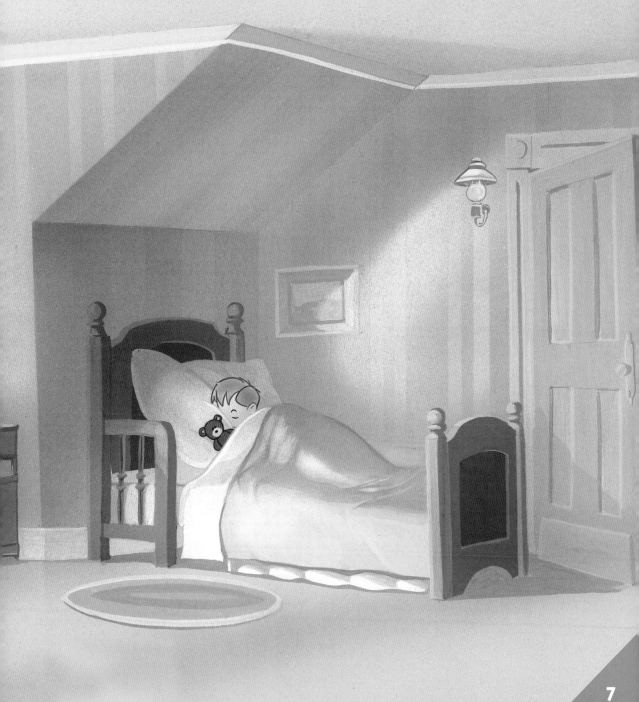

John, Wendy, and young Michael see a boy.

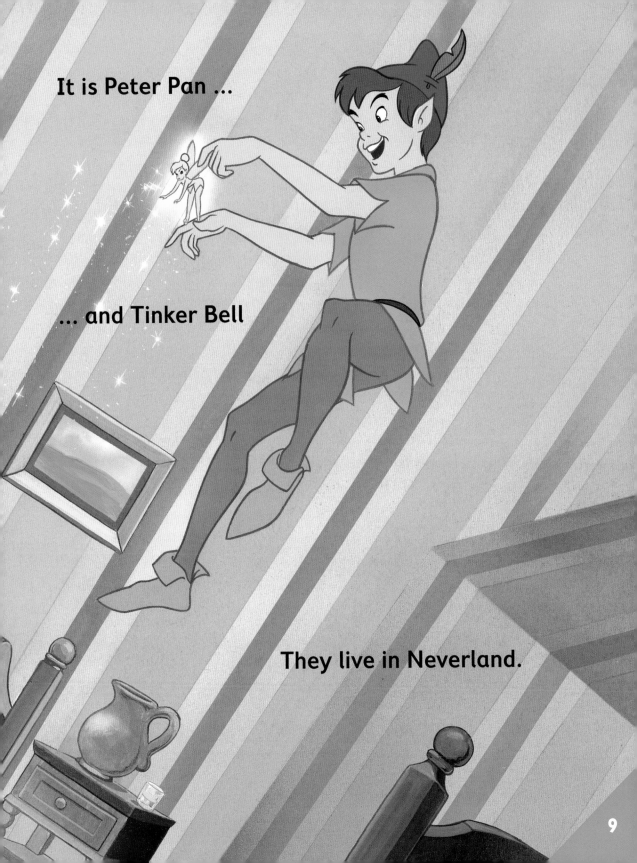

It is Peter Pan ...

... and Tinker Bell

They live in Neverland.

9

Neverland is magical.

Peter Pan, Tinker Bell, and the children fly to Neverland.

Peter Pan, Tinker Bell, and the children fly and fly.
They see Big Ben. They are happy.

Bye bye, London!

Hello, Neverland!

It is beautiful.

Activities

Before You Read

1 Look at pages 2 and 3. Find the children.

After You Read

1 Look at the pictures. Point to:

Wendy   John   Michael   Peter Pan   Tinker Bell

2 Complete. Choose words from the box.

children   London   magical   Neverland   fly

1 Wendy, John, and Michael are from ....
2 The .... live in a big house.
3 Peter Pan and Tinker Bell are from ....
4 Peter Pan and Tinker Bell .... in the bedroom.
5 Neverland is ....

3 Write yes (Y) or no (N).
1 There are two children. ☐   2 Peter Pan has a blue hat. ☐
3 The children are happy. ☐   4 They fly to Peterland. ☐

Pearson Education Limited
Edinburgh Gate, Harlow,
Essex CM20 2JE, England
and Associated Companies throughout the world.

ISBN: 978-1-4082-8852-8

This edition first published by Pearson Education Ltd 2012

1 3 5 7 9 10 8 6 4 2

Text copyright © Pearson Education Ltd 2012
Copyright © 2012 Disney Enterprises, Inc. All rights reserved.

The moral rights of the author have been asserted
in accordance with the Copyright Designs and Patents Act 1988

Set in 19/23pt OT Fiendstar Semibold
Printed in China
SWTC/01

Published by Pearson Education Ltd in association with
Penguin Books Ltd, both companies being subsidiaries of Pearson Plc

For a complete list of the titles available in the Penguin Kids series please go to www.penguinreaders.com.
Alternatively, write to your local Pearson Longman office or to: Penguin Readers Marketing Department,
Pearson Education, Edinburgh Gate, Harlow, Essex CM20 2JE, England.